POLYA TYPE
DISTRIBUTIONS
IN RENEWAL THEORY

1959 Award Winner

THE FORD FOUNDATION DOCTORAL DISSERTATION SERIES

A dissertation submitted in partial fulfillment of the requirements for the degree of Doctor of Philosophy at Stanford University

POLYA TYPE DISTRIBUTIONS IN RENEWAL THEORY

. . . *With an Application to an Inventory Problem*

FRANK PROSCHAN

Sylvania Electric Products Inc.
Mountain View, California

1960

PRENTICE-HALL, INC.

Englewood Cliffs, N. J.

Foreword

This volume is one of five doctoral dissertations selected for publication in the first annual Doctoral Dissertation Competition sponsored by the Program in Economic Development and Administration of The Ford Foundation. The winning dissertations were completed during the academic year 1958-59 by doctoral candidates in business administration and doctoral candidates in the social sciences and other fields relevant to the study of problems of business.

The dissertation competition is intended to generalize standards of excellence in research on business by graduate students. It should give widespread professional recognition to persons recently awarded doctorates in business whose dissertation research is especially distinguished by its analytical content and strong roots in underlying disciplines. It is also intended to give recognition to a select number of persons outside business schools who in their doctoral dissertations pursued with distinction interests relevant to business.

The dissertations selected include, in addition to Dr. Proschan's monograph:

Computer Models of the Shoe, Leather, Hide Sequence
>>Kalman J. Cohen
>>Graduate School of Industrial Administration
>>Carnegie Institute of Technology

Budget Control and Cost Behavior
>>Andrew C. Stedry
>>Graduate School of Industrial Administration
>>Carnegie Institute of Technology

Some Personality Determinants of the Effects of Participation
>>Victor H. Vroom
>>Department of Psychology
>>University of Michigan

The Structure of a Retail Market and the Market Behavior of Retail Units
>>Bob R. Holdren
>>Department of Economics
>>Yale University

The many high-quality dissertations submitted were judged by the most exacting professional standards. Specific criteria included:

a. Importance of the problem and originality of approach;
b. Use of the most appropriate and powerful tools of analysis;
c. Clear relation to the relevant theoretical framework or a contribution to theory;
d. Direct relevance to the practice of business or management;
e. Clarity and effectiveness of presentation.

An examination of all five volumes in this series will reveal that four of the five make considerable use of mathematical and statistical tools. This reflects the increasing importance of modern quantitative methods in the study of business. On the other hand, the use of quantitative techniques should certainly not be considered a *sine qua non* of rigorous research in business. It is hoped that in future years it will be possible to select for publication a greater number of nonmathematical dissertations of the highest quality.

On behalf of The Ford Foundation, I wish to express my sincere appreciation to the Editorial Committee for its painstaking effort in selecting the winning dissertations. The scholars who served as members of the Committee for the first year's competition were Robert Ferber, Research Professor of Economics, University of Illinois; Sherman J. Maisel, Professor of Business Administration, University of California (Berkeley); and William Foote Whyte, Professor, New York State School of Industrial and Labor Relations, Cornell University.

The work of the Editorial Committee was materially aided by a group of six readers, who spent hundreds of hours in conscientious examination of the dissertations submitted. The Foundation and the Committee wish to thank Professors Austin C. Hoggatt and Julius Margolis of the University of California (Berkeley), Henry A. Landsberger and Seymour Smidt of Cornell University, and Vernon K. Zimmerman and Thomas A. Yancey of the University of Illinois for their service as readers in the first year of the competition.

Finally, my colleagues and I wish to acknowledge the substantial contribution of Prentice-Hall, Inc., to the publication and distribution of the selected dissertations.

THOMAS H. CARROLL
VICE PRESIDENT
THE FORD FOUNDATION

New York, New York
January, 1960

Preface

For want of a nail, the shoe was lost,
For want of a shoe, the horse was lost,
For want of a horse, the rider was lost,
For want of a rider, the battle was lost,
For want of a battle, the kingdom was lost,
And all for the want of a horseshoenail.
— Margaret de Angelis, *Mother Goose*

Unfortunately, to this day the problem remains — if anything even worse than before. Many a critically important electronic "kingdom," such as a radar, a computer, or a missile system, has been rendered useless during critical periods of need because of the shortage of an electronic "nail," say a ten cent resistor. This dissertation attempts to prevent the loss of "kingdoms" by showing how to insure that enough "nails" are on hand — without spending a king's ransom.

It has become increasingly apparent that one of the key problems facing large military and industrial organizations is to prevent the paralysis of complex systems in the field resulting from the shortage of some essential component. The problem stems from the fact that component failure is essentially random, so that one cannot predict with certainty the number of replacements required for each type of essential component. If the system has been in operation for some time, then experience may have been accumulated as to the level of demand for replacements; in this case, rational procedures exist for determining sensible spare part kits. If, however, the system is new, with no operating experience available as to the level of demand for replacements, the problem becomes quite difficult. If, in addition, the number and variety of essential components is great, and the total amount of money available to purchase spare parts is limited, then the problem may seem insuperable. And yet, its solution may be just as important in determining the effectiveness of the system as the solution of the scientific and engineering problems encountered in the original design and construction of the system.

The dissertation develops a mathematical method for the determination of optimal spare part kits — optimal, in the sense that for a given

vii

expenditure for spare parts, maximum assurance is achieved against system shutdown due to shortage of essential components. The only input data needed to compute the composition of an optimal kit are (a) the numbers of essential components of each type operating at various levels of intensity, (b) the corresponding probability distributions of component life, and (c) the unit cost for each component type. The actual computation is reduced to a straightforward procedure, and even for large, complicated systems can be performed on an electronic computer in a short space of time (e.g., for a system containing many simultaneously operating units of each of 200 different essential component types, twenty minutes on an IBM 650 was sufficient to provide optimal kits corresponding to 5 different budgets).

It is gratifying to be able to report that the procedure has actually been put into practice to compute optimal spare part kits for (a) several Signal Corps prototype systems by the Electronic Defense Laboratory, Sylvania Electric Products, Inc., (b) large computer systems in the BMEWS program by Data Processing Operations, Sylvania Electric Products, Inc., (c) a naval range finder developed by the University of Washington, and (d) an Air Force space platform program at the Sperry Gyroscope Co. In addition, the same mathematical model is being used to solve an analogous problem in reliability at the Amherst Engineering Laboratory, Sylvania Electric Products, Inc. under a naval contract — namely, to determine the number of redundant standby units of each essential component needed to achieve maximum system reliability under a weight (or space) constraint.

In the course of obtaining the solution presented in the dissertation, a number of new mathematical results in renewal theory were obtained. These results have additional applications in inventory and reliability theory. A paper by S. Karlin and F. Proschan generalizing these results and giving applications to mathematics, statistics, and inventory theory is to appear in the *Annals of Mathematical Statistics* under the title "Polya Type Distributions of Convolutions."

FRANK PROSCHAN

Contents

ix

CHAPTER 5

EXPONENTIAL FAILURE DISTRIBUTIONS   *28*

CHAPTER 6

CONVOLUTIONS WHEN THE RANDOM VARIABLE IS NOT NECESSARILY POSITIVE   *33*

I would like to acknowledge the inspiration and generous assistance provided by my thesis advisor Professor Herbert Scarf and the stimulation and helpful advice gained in the course of many discussions with Professor Samuel Karlin.

CHAPTER 1

Introduction and Summary

This thesis has two purposes: (a) to solve an important practical problem arising in inventory theory; (b) to present some new results on Polya Type distributions arising in renewal theory. Since the derivation of the solution of the inventory problem led to the results obtained in renewal theory, it will be motivating to present the inventory problem first.

1.1. Inventory Problem

A complex system is to be placed in the field for a period of time t_0. When a component fails, it is instantly replaced by a spare, if available. The components considered operate independently (i.e., failure of one does not influence failure of any other), and are essential to continued system operation, so that a shortage of any component considered results in system shutdown. Only the spares originally provided may be used for replacements; i.e., no resupply of spares can occur during the period.

The system contains d_i components of type i, $i = 1, 2, \cdots, k$, simultaneously operating. Different components of a given type may be used at different levels of intensity, so that the length of life of the jth component of type i (component i, j) and its replacements are independent random variables with density $f_{ij}(t)$,

1

$j = 1, \cdots, d_i;\ i = 1, \cdots, k$. The scheduled length of time t_{ij} that component i, j and its replacements must operate during t_0 is a constant, $j = 1, \cdots, d_i;\ i = 1, \cdots, k$. Finally, the cost of a single unit of type i is $c_i, i = 1, \cdots, k$.

What choice of n_i, the number of spares of type i initially provided, $i = 1, \cdots, k$, will yield maximum assurance of continued system operation (i.e., no shortage of any essential component) during the period $[0, t_0]$ at a total cost for spares $c(n_1, \cdots, n_k) = \sum_{i=1}^{k} n_i c_i \leq c_0$, a constant?

1.2. Related Models

Related models in the spare parts problem have been treated in (3), (4), and (5). In these models the expected total of weighted shortages is minimized subject to a linear weight or cost restraint, with the demand probability density for spares assumed a priori. In our model we maximize assurance of continued system operation by optimal allocation of spares likewise subject to a linear restraint, but with the demand for spares, instead of being assumed a priori, *generated by failure of operating units* following known probability distributions. Thus, to obtain the composition of the optimal spare parts kit we use information about component failure distributions rather than information about component demand distributions. In the typical situation under consideration — a new system under experimentation for a single period in the field — we are thus given the opportunity to use information we may have, component failure rates, rather than being called upon to provide information we may not have, component demand distributions. Our choice of probability of continued system operation as the figure of merit to be maximized is especially relevant in military applications, where a penalty cost is often difficult to determine.

1.3. Sketch of Results

In Chapter 2 we present a procedure for obtaining the maximizing set $n_1^*, \cdots, n_k^*$ for the case $Q_i(n + 1)/Q_i(n)$ a decreasing function of n, where $Q_i(n)$ is the probability that n or less failures of type i occur during $[0, t_0]$, $i = 1, \cdots, k$. In Chapter 3 we show that $Q_i(n + 1)/Q_i(n)$ *is* a decreasing function of n whenever each $f_{ij}(t)$ for $j = 1, \cdots, d_i$ is a density having a monotone likelihood ratio in differences of t; since the class of monotone likelihood ratio densities includes most of the standard probability densities, the inventory problem above may be considered solved.

In order to demonstrate that "$f_{ij}(t)$, a monotone likelihood ratio density for each $j = 1, \cdots, d_i$," implies "$Q_i(n + 1)/Q_i(n)$ a decreasing function of n," we derive some results of independent interest in renewal theory, of the following type (see Chapters 3 and 4).

Theorem. If $f_i(t)$ is a Polya frequency function of order k having a continuous first derivative, with $f_i(t) = 0$ for $t < 0$, for $i = 1, 2, \cdots$, then $p'(n, t)$, the convolution of f_1 with f_2 with $\cdots$ with f_n, is a Polya Type density of order k in n and t, where n ranges over $1, 2, \cdots$.

Theorem. If $f_i(t)$ are monotone likelihood ratio densities in differences of t with $f_i(t) = 0$ for $t < 0$, $i = 1, 2, \cdots$, then $\Delta P'(n, t)$ $= \int_t^\infty p'(n + 1, u)du - \int_t^\infty p'(n, u)du$ has the monotone likelihood ratio property in n and t jointly, and also in differences of n. ($\Delta P'(n, t)$ is the probability that precisely n events occur during $[0, t]$ if the interval between the i-1st and ith event is an independent observation from f_i, $i = 1, 2, \cdots$.)

We then apply these theorems to the inventory problem and show how to solve more general models in which the t_{ij} are random variables, the original components are aged, and in which the replacements may have different failure densities.

In Chapter 5 we show how to compute with explicit formulas the composition of the optimal spare parts kit for the most commonly occurring real life situation; namely, where component failure densities are exponential. A numerical example is presented to illustrate the method. Finally, we point out how the mathematical model may be applied in achieving maximum reliability in the design of complex systems.

In Chapter 6 we consider the extension of the theorems obtained for positive random variables to the more general case in which the random variables may be positive or negative. The corresponding conclusions are considerably weaker in the latter case.

CHAPTER 2

Maximizing a Nonlinear Function Subject to a Linear Constraint

2.1. Maximizing $Q(n)$ as a Function of the $Q_i(n)$

Let $Q_i(n)$ = probability that n or less failures of type i occur during $[0, t_0]$, $i = 1, \cdots, k$.

$n = n_1, n_2, \cdots, n_k$, a vector.

$Q(n)$ = probability that no shortage is experienced for any of the k types during $[0, t_0]$ given an initial kit of composition n.

$c(n)$ = total cost of a spare parts kit composed of n_i units of type i, $i = 1, 2, \cdots, k$.

Since components operate independently and failure of any one causes system shutdown, the probability of continued system operation during $[0, t_0]$ is given by

$$Q(n) = \prod_{i=1}^{k} Q_i(n_i) \qquad (2.1)$$

Also, we note that

$$c(n) = \sum_{i=1}^{k} n_i c_i \qquad (2.2)$$

We wish to maximize $Q(n)$ subject to

$$\sum_{i=1}^{k} n_i c_i \leq c_0 \quad \text{and} \quad n_i \geq 0, \, i = 1, \cdots, k \qquad (2.3)$$

Define: $R_i(n) = \ln Q_i(n)$ and $R(\boldsymbol{n}) = \ln Q(\boldsymbol{n})$. Then, it is equivalent to maximize $R(\boldsymbol{n})$ subject to (2.3).

Maximizing a nonlinear function $R(\boldsymbol{n})$ subject to linear restraints (2.3) is a special case of nonlinear programming, treated in (10). In (10) the theorems are developed in detail for continuous variables. In our problem we are dealing with discrete variables, $n_1, \cdots, n_k$. Thus we shall independently derive the required theorems.

Define $\Delta R_i(n) = R_i(n+1) - R_i(n)$ for $n = 0, 1, 2, \cdots$; $i = 1, 2, \cdots, k$. Then we shall show in Theorem 2.1 and its corollary below that when $\Delta R_i(n)$ decreasing for $i = 1, \cdots, k$ we may obtain the solution to our inventory problem by following Procedure 1.

Procedure 1. Let $\Delta R_i(n)$ be a decreasing function of n for $i = 1, \cdots, k$. For arbitrary $r > 0$, for those i such that $\Delta R_i(0) < rc_i$, define $n_i^*(r) = 0$; for the remaining i, define $n_i^*(r)$ as 1 plus largest n such that $\Delta R_i(n) \geq rc_i$. Compute $c(\boldsymbol{n}^*(r)) = \sum_{i=1}^{k} c_i n_i^*(r)$. Let r_0 be the value of r yielding maximum $c(\boldsymbol{n}^*(r)) \leq c_0$. Then $\boldsymbol{n}^*(r_0)$ is the spares kit corresponding to a budget restraint of c_0.

The following theorem shows $\boldsymbol{n}^*$ is optimal when c_0 is one of the values assumed by $c(\boldsymbol{n}^*(r))$ as r varies over $(0, \infty)$.

Theorem 2.1. $\boldsymbol{n}^*$ maximizes $R(\boldsymbol{n})$ among all $\boldsymbol{n}$ such that $c(\boldsymbol{n}) \leq c(\boldsymbol{n}^*)$, $\boldsymbol{n} \geq 0$.

Proof. We will show for any $0 \leq \boldsymbol{n} \not\equiv \boldsymbol{n}^*$ for which $c(\boldsymbol{n}) \leq c(\boldsymbol{n}^*)$ that $R(\boldsymbol{n}) \leq R(\boldsymbol{n}^*)$. Suppose $n_i > n_i^*$ for i in I_1, $n_i < n_i^*$ for i in I_2, where I_1, I_2 are subsets of $\{1, 2, \cdots, k\}$. Since $\Delta R_i(n_i)$ is a decreasing function of n_i by assumption, then

$$\Delta R_i(n_i^* + j) \leq rc_i \quad \text{for } i \text{ in } I_1, j = 0, 1, 2, \cdots, n_i - n_i^* - 1 \quad (2.4a)$$

Similarly

$$\Delta R_i(n_i^* - j) \geq rc_i \quad \text{for } i \text{ in } I_2, j = 1, 2, \cdots, n_i^* - n_i \quad (2.4b)$$

Hence

$$R(\boldsymbol{n}) - R(\boldsymbol{n}^*) = \sum_{i \text{ in } I_1} \sum_{j=0}^{n_i - n_i^* - 1} \Delta R_i(n_i^* + j) - \sum_{i \text{ in } I_2} \sum_{j=1}^{n_i^* - n_i} \Delta R_i(n_i^* - j)$$

$$\leq r \sum_{i \text{ in } I_1} (n_i - n_i^*)c_i - r \sum_{i \text{ in } I_2} (n_i^* - n_i)c_i = r \sum_{i=1}^{k} (n_i - n_i^*)c_i$$

$$= r\{c(\boldsymbol{n}) - c(\boldsymbol{n}^*)\}$$

But $r > 0$ and $c(\boldsymbol{n}) - c(\boldsymbol{n}^*) \leq 0$. Hence $R(\boldsymbol{n}) \leq R(\boldsymbol{n}^*)$.   QED

(In the remainder of this chapter we shall confine attention to the case in which $\Delta R_i(n)$ is a decreasing function of n for $i = 1, \cdots, k$. In Chapter 3 we derive a sufficient condition for $\Delta R_i(n)$ decreasing.)

It follows that a given value of r yields a kit composition $\boldsymbol{n}^*(r)$ which solves the original inventory problem for the particular case $c_0 = \sum_{i=1}^{k} c_i n_i^*(r)$. Hence by varying r over the interval $(0, \infty)$, we may obtain solutions corresponding to a c_0 equal to any of the different (discrete) values $\sum_{i=1}^{k} c_i n_i^*(r)$ may assume. We shall refer to any vector $\boldsymbol{n}^*$ obtained by Procedure 1 as an *optimal point* or an *optimal kit*.

For values of c_0 different from any of the $c(\boldsymbol{n}^*)$, Procedure 1 may provide only an approximate solution because of the discrete nature of the variables $n_1, \cdots, n_k$; the bound on the error is given in the corollary below, and in most practical problems will be small.

Corollary. For $c_0 \neq c(\boldsymbol{n}^*(r))$ for all $r > 0$,

$$\max_{\substack{c(\boldsymbol{n}) \leq c_0 \\ \boldsymbol{n} \geq 0}} Q(\boldsymbol{n}) - Q(\boldsymbol{n}^*(r_0)) \leq Q(\boldsymbol{n}') - Q(\boldsymbol{n}^*(r_0))$$

where $c(\boldsymbol{n}') = \min_{c(\boldsymbol{n}^*) > c_0} c(\boldsymbol{n}^*)$. ($\boldsymbol{n}'$ represents the cheapest optimal kit of higher cost than c_0.)

Proof. By Theorem 2.1, $R(n') \geq R(n)$ for all $n \geq 0$ such that $c(n) \leq c_0 < c(n')$. Hence $Q(n') \geq Q(n)$ for all $n \geq 0$ such that $c(n) \leq c_0 < c(n')$. Thus $Q(n') \geq \max_{\substack{c(n) \leq c_0 \\ n \geq 0}} Q(n)$. Hence the theorem.   QED

Thus the error in using Procedure 1 is at most the difference in protection achieved by the two adjacent optimal kits whose costs straddle the specified c_0. This motivates the following alternate procedure for obtaining in succession the same set of optimal points as are obtained by Procedure 1.

Procedure 2. First note that $(0, \cdots, 0)$ is an optimal point (corresponding to $c_0 = 0$). Next let n^* be any optimal point. Compute $\Delta R_i(n_i^*)/c_i$ for $i = 1, \cdots, k$. If the αth ratio is the largest, the next optimal point to the right of n^* is $(n_1^*, \cdots, n_{\alpha-1}^*, n_\alpha^* + 1, n_{\alpha+1}^*, \cdots, n_k^*)$, as will be proved in Theorem 2.2. (We shall designate the immediate successor of an optimal point n^* by $n^{*(\alpha)}$, where α is the (only) coordinate that has changed.)

Theorem 2.2. Any point obtainable by Procedure 1 is obtainable by Procedure 2, and conversely.

Proof. Let n^* be a point obtainable by Procedure 2. Suppose n^* is obtained from the preceding point on the left by a change in the αth coordinate. Set $r_0 = \Delta R_\alpha(n_\alpha^* - 1)/c_\alpha$. Thus

$$\Delta R_\alpha(n_\alpha^*)/c_\alpha < r_0 \leq \Delta R_\alpha(n_\alpha^* - 1)/c_\alpha \qquad (2.5)$$

since $\Delta R_\alpha(n)$ is decreasing. Also we know

$$\Delta R_i(n_i^*)/c_i < r_0 \text{ for all } i \neq \alpha \qquad (2.6)$$

Now if there existed β such that $\Delta R_\beta(n_\beta^* - 1)/c_\beta < r_0 \leq \Delta R_\alpha(n_\alpha^* - 1)/c_\alpha$, there would be a point lying to the left of n^* whose αth coordinate would be n_α^* and whose βth coordinate would be $\leq n_\beta^* - 1$ (i.e., in computing successive points, the αth coordinate would change before the βth). This would contradict the assumption that n^* is obtained from the preceding point on the left by a change in the αth coordinate. Thus we conclude that

$$\Delta R_i(n_i^* - 1)/c_i \geq r_0 \quad \text{for all } i \neq \alpha \qquad (2.7)$$

From (2.5), (2.6), and (2.7), we see that n^* is obtainable by Procedure 1.

Next, let n^* and $n^{*(\alpha)}$ be a pair of successive points obtained by using Procedure 2. We shall show that there are no points lying between them obtainable by Procedure 1. Assume there is such a point m^* with $r = r_0$. For at least one coordinate of m^* other than the αth, say the βth, we thus have either (1) $m_\beta^* > n_\beta^*$, or (2) $m_\beta^* \leq n_\beta^*$. Assume (1). Then the βth coordinate of n^*, m^*, and $n^{*(\alpha)}$ are, respectively, n_β^*, m_β^*, and n_β^*. Since n^* and $n^{*(\alpha)}$ are obtainable by Procedure 2, we have just shown that each is obtainable by Procedure 1. Hence there is an $r = r_1$ and an $r = r_2$ with $r_1 > r_2$ associated with n^* and $n^{*(\alpha)}$ respectively with the property that $\Delta R_\beta(n_\beta^* - 1)/c_\beta \geq r_1$ and $\Delta R_\beta(n_\beta^*)/c_\beta < r_2$. Also $\Delta R_\beta(m_\beta^*)/c_\beta \geq r_0$, while $\Delta R_\beta(m_\beta^*)/c_\beta < r_0$. But m^* lies to the left of $n^{*(\alpha)}$, so that $r_0 > r_2$; hence we have $\Delta R_\beta(n_\beta^*)/c_\beta < r_2 < r_0 \leq \Delta R_\beta(m_\beta^* - 1)/c_\beta$. This is impossible since $n_\beta^* \leq m_\beta^* - 1$. A similar argument rules out (2). Thus there are no points obtainable by Procedure 1 lying between n^* and $n^{*(\alpha)}$. This means that every point obtainable by Procedure 1 is obtainable by Procedure 2.   QED

Procedure 2 represents a systematic way of obtaining all optimal points needed, and it is more convenient for machine computation. Actually, the two methods may be usefully combined in the following commonly occurring situation. Suppose there is no single value of c_0 specified. Rather, suppose what is desired is a curve (*optimal curve*) showing maximum protection $Q(n^*)$ against system shutdown as a function of total cost $c(n^*)$ for spares. To obtain this curve, compute an optimal point by Procedure 1 near the lower end of the range of interest of protection or cost (several trial values of r may have to be used). Then proceed systematically up the curve by Procedure 2. The following theorem furnishes some helpful information about the number of points in any portion of the optimal curve.

Theorem 2.3. The number of points on the optimal curve between any two distinct optimal points m^* and n^* (with $m^* \leq n^*$, say) is $\sum_{i=1}^{k} (n_i^* - m_i^*) - 1$.

Proof. By Procedure 2 we get successive points by changing one coordinate at a time. The number of such changes in going from m^* to n^* is $\sum_{i=1}^{k} (n_i^* - m_i^*)$. Excluding the last change which results in n^*, we find that there are $\sum_{i=1}^{k} (n_i^* - m_i^*) - 1$ optimal points between m^* and n^*.   QED

2.2. Expressing $Q_i(n)$ as a Function of the f_{ij}

So far, we have shown how the problem may be solved in terms of $Q_i(n)$, $i = 1, \cdots, k$, under the assumption $Q_i(n + 1)/Q_i(n)$ decreasing for each i. In the remainder of this section we shall obtain the relationship between the $Q_i(n)$ and the underlying failure densities $f_{ij}(t)$. Clearly the random process describing successive replacement of failed components is a renewal process; thus the continued operation of the complex system may be thought of as a set of independent renewal processes.

For $j = 1, \cdots, d_i;$ $i = 1, \cdots, k;$ $-\infty < t < \infty$, let

$$p_{ij}(1, t) = f_{ij}(t)$$

$$p_{ij}(2, t) = \int_{-\infty}^{\infty} f_{ij}(\theta) f_{ij}(t - \theta) d\theta$$

$\cdots$

$$p_{ij}(n, t) = \int_{-\infty}^{\infty} f_{ij}(\theta) p_{ij}(n - 1, t - \theta) d\theta \qquad \text{for } n = 3, 4, \cdots$$

$$P_{ij}(n, t) = \int_{t}^{\infty} p_{ij}(n, \theta) d\theta \qquad \text{for } n = 1, 2, \cdots$$

$$\Delta P_{ij}(n, t) = \begin{cases} P_{ij}(1, t) & \text{for } n = 0 \\ P_{ij}(n + 1, t) - P_{ij}(n, t) & \text{for } n = 1, 2, \cdots \end{cases}$$

$q_i(n) =$ probability of exactly n failures of component type i.

Thus $p_{ij}(n, t)$, being the n-fold convolution of $f_{ij}(t)$, represents the probability density for the combined life of the original i, j component and $n - 1$ replacements; as a consequence, $P_{ij}(n, t_{ij})$ is the probability that $n - 1$ or less spares will be used in replacing the i, j component during the specified t_{ij} units of time. From the definition of $\Delta P_{ij}(n, t_{ij})$, we know from renewal theory (1, p. 272) that $\Delta P_{ij}(n, t_{ij})$ represents the probability that *exactly* n spares will be required during the t_{ij} units of time scheduled for component i, j (and its replacements). Next, since the total number of spares of type i required for continued system operation during $[0, t_0]$ is simply the sum of the numbers required to replace component i, j for $j = 1, 2, \cdots, d_i$, we have

$$q_i(n) = \Delta P_{i1}(n, t_{i1}) * \Delta P_{i2}(n, t_{i2}) \cdots * \Delta P_{id_i}(n, t_{id_i}) \qquad (2.8)$$

where the convolution (indicated by *) is taken in the first argument of the $\Delta P_{ij}(n, t_{ij})$. Finally, $Q_i(n)$, the probability of n or less failures of type i during $[0, t_0]$, is clearly given by

$$Q_i(n) = \sum_{m=0}^{n} q_i(m) \qquad (2.9)$$

so that $q_i(n)$ represents the density and $Q_i(n)$ the distribution function for the total number of failures (or equivalently, the total number of spares required) of type i during $[0, t_0]$.

Thus following the definitions above and (2.8) and (2.9), we may compute according to standard procedures (possibly somewhat tediously) the values of $Q_i(n)$ as a function of the f_{ij}. From the values of $Q_i(n)$, using either Procedure 1 or Procedure 2 (or a combination), we may solve the original inventory problem *provided $Q_i(n + 1)/Q_i(n)$ is decreasing*. In the next section, we shall demonstrate that $Q_i(n + 1)/Q_i(n)$ decreases whenever the $f_{ij}(t)$ are monotone likelihood ratio densities in differences of t.

CHAPTER 3

Polya Type Distributions
in Renewal Theory

3.1. Preliminaries

According to (8, p. 282) a family of distributions

$$F(x, \theta) = \beta(\theta) \int_{-\infty}^{x} f(t, \theta) d\mu(t)$$

of a real random variable X depending on a real parameter θ is said to be Polya Type k ($F(x, \theta)$ is PT_k) if

$$0 \leq \begin{vmatrix} f(x_1, \theta_1) \cdots f(x_1, \theta_m) \\ \cdot \qquad \qquad \cdot \\ \cdot \qquad \qquad \cdot \\ \cdot \qquad \qquad \cdot \\ f(x_m, \theta_1) \cdots f(x_m, \theta_m) \end{vmatrix} \qquad \text{(symbolized hereafter by } |f(x_i, \theta_j)|)$$

for every $1 \leq m \leq k$ and all $x_1 < x_2 < \cdots < x_m$, and $\theta_1 < \theta_2 < \cdots < \theta_m$. If the family of distributions $F(x, \theta)$ is PT_k for every k, then we say that the family is PT_∞. We shall say that $f(x, \theta)$ is $PT_k(\infty)$ if $F(x, \theta)$ belongs to $PT_k(\infty)$.

For $k = 1$, 2 the conditions of being PT_k reduce to familiar ones. f is PT_1 if and only if $f(x, \theta) \geq 0$ for all x and θ. f is PT_2 if and only if it has a monotone likelihood ratio.

Karlin uses the variation diminishing properties of Polya Type functions to obtain some fundamental results in statistical decision theory.

We shall find it useful to include in the class of PT_k, functions $P(\eta, t) = \int_t^\infty p(\eta, u)du$, where $p(\eta, u)$ is a probability density and η a real valued parameter, if $|P(\eta_i, t_j)| \geq 0$ for all $\eta_1 < \cdots < \eta_m$ and $t_1 < \cdots < t_m$, $1 \leq m \leq k$.

If a PT_k function $F(x, \theta)$ is a function $G(x - \theta)$ of the difference of x and θ, we shall refer to it as a *Polya frequency function of order k* (G is Pff_k).

An important property of Polya Type functions as defined in (8) is that the convolution of a PT_m function and a PT_n function yields a $PT_{\min(m, n)}$ function (9, Lemma 5). We note that this property holds for our slightly more inclusive class of PT functions (assuming the integral involved is finite).

Lemma 3.1. Let $f(x, \theta)$ be PT_m, $g(\theta, \omega)$ be PT_n, and let $h(x, \omega) = \int f(x, \theta)\, g(\theta, \omega)d\theta < \infty$. Then $h(x, \omega)$ is $PT_{\min(m, n)}$.

Proof. The proof is as in (9).

Let $p(n, t)$ be the n-fold convolution of the density $f(t)$ for $n = 1, 2, \cdots$; i.e., $p(1, t) = f(t)$; $p(2, t) = \int f(t - \theta)\, f(\theta)\, d\theta$; $\cdots$; $p(n + 1, t) = \int p(n, t - \theta) f(\theta)\, d\theta$; $\cdots$. Then, we have immediately:

Lemma 3.2. If $f(t)$ is Pff_k, then $p(n, t)$ is Pff_k in t for $n = 1, 2, \cdots$.

Proof. This follows from repeated application of Lemma 3.1.

Next, define $H(t) = \begin{cases} 1 & \text{if } t \leq 0 \\ 0 & \text{if } t > 0 \end{cases}$. Then we may show:

Lemma 3.3. $H(t)$ is Pff_∞.

Proof. The proof is as in (12, p. 335). For any k, with $t_1 < \cdots < t_k$, $\theta_1 < \cdots < \theta_k$; $D_k = |H(t_i - \theta_j)|$ of order k, has these properties.

(1) The elements are 0 or 1.

(2) The elements in every row are non-decreasing.

(3) The elements in every column are non-increasing.

From this it follows that $D_k = 0$ or D_k is of the form

$$\begin{vmatrix} 1 & 1 & 1 & \cdots & 1 \\ 0 & 1 & 1 & \cdots & 1 \\ 0 & 0 & 1 & \cdots & 1 \\ \cdot & \cdot & \cdot & \cdots & \cdot \\ 0 & 0 & 0 & \cdots & 1 \end{vmatrix} = 1$$

QED

Next define $P(n, t) = \begin{cases} 0 \text{ for } n < 0 \\ H(t) \text{ for } n = 0 \\ \int_t^\infty p(n, u)du \text{ for } n \geq 1. \end{cases}$

Then, we obtain immediately:

Lemma 3.4. If $f(t)$ is Pff_k, then $P(n, t)$ is Pff_k in t for $n = 1$, 2, $\cdots$.

Proof. For $n = 1, 2, \cdots, P(n, t) = \int_{-\infty}^\infty p(n, \omega)P(0, t - \omega)d\omega$ so that the conclusion follows from Lemmas 3.1, 3.2, and 3.3.   QED

3.2. New Results

A key theorem follows from these lemmas.

Theorem 3.1. If $f(t)$ is Pff_k with $f(t) = 0$ for $t < 0$, then $P(n, t)$ is PT_k, where n ranges over the values 0, 1, 2, $\cdots$.

Proof. We shall use an inductive proof. First we demonstrate $P(n, t)$ is PT_2. Let $n_1 < n_2$, $t_1 < t_2$ and define

$$D_2 = \begin{vmatrix} P(n_1, t_1) & P(n_1, t_2) \\ P(n_2, t_1) & P(n_2, t_2) \end{vmatrix}$$

(a) Let $n_1 = 0$. If $t_1 > 0$, the first row consists of 0's so that $D_2 = 0$. If $t_1 \leq 0$, $D_2 = P(n_2, t_2) - P(n_1, t_2) \geq 0$.

(b) Let $n_1 > 0$. Then for $t_1 < 0$, $D_2 = P(n_2, t_2) - P(n_1, t_2) \geq 0$.

For

$$t_1 \geq 0, \, D_2 = \int \begin{vmatrix} P(n_1, t_1) & P(n_1, t_1 - \theta) \\ P(n_1, t_2) & P(n_1, t_2 - \theta) \end{vmatrix} p(n_2 - n_1, \theta) d\theta \geq 0$$

by Lemma 3.4.   (3.1)

Now assume we have shown $P(n, t)$ is PT_{m-1} for $m \leq k$. We shall show that this implies $P(n, t)$ is PT_m. From this it will follow that $P(n, t)$ is PT_k.

Define $\Delta_j = t_{j+1} - t_1, j = 1, 2, \cdots, m - 1$. For $t_1 < t_2 < \cdots < t_m, 0 < n_1 < n_2 < \cdots < n_{m-1}$, form

$$D_m = \begin{vmatrix} P(n, t_1) & P(n + n_1, t_1) & \cdots & P(n + n_{m-1}, t_1) \\ P(n, t_2) & P(n + n_1, t_2) & \cdots & P(n + n_{m-1}, t_2) \\ \cdots & \cdots & \cdots & \cdots \\ P(n, t_m) & P(n + n_1, t_m) & \cdots & P(n + n_{m-1}, t_m) \end{vmatrix}$$

Let $n = 0$.

(a) $t_1 > 0$ implies the first column consists of 0's. Hence $D_m = 0$.

(b) $t_1 \leq 0 < t_2$ implies all entries in the first column are 0, except the first, which is 1. Thus $D_m \geq 0$ by inductive hypothesis.

(c) $t_1 < t_2 \leq 0$ implies the first two rows consist of 1's, so that $D_m = 0$.

Hence we let $n > 0$. Then

$$D_m = \begin{vmatrix} \int p(n, \theta) P(0, t_1 - \theta) d\theta & \int p(n, \theta) P(n_1, t_1 - \theta) d\theta \cdots \int p(n, \theta) P(n_{m-1}, t_1 - \theta) d\theta \\ \int p(n, \theta + \Delta_1) P(0, t_1 - \theta) d\theta & \int p(n, \theta + \Delta_1) P(n_1, t_1 - \theta) d\theta \cdots \int p(n, \theta + \Delta_1) P(n_{m-1}, t_1 - \theta) d\theta \\ \cdots & \cdots & \cdots & \cdots \\ \int p(n, \theta + \Delta_{m-1}) P(0, t_1 - \theta) d\theta & \int p(n, \theta + \Delta_{m-1}) P(n_1, t_1 - \theta) d\theta \cdots \int p(n, \theta + \Delta_{m-1}) P(n_{m-1}, t_1 - \theta) d\theta \end{vmatrix}$$

Thus

$$D_m = \int \cdots \int_{\theta_1 < \cdots < \theta_m} D'D'' d\theta_1 \cdots d\theta_m \qquad (3.2)$$

where

$$D' = \begin{vmatrix} p(n, \theta_1) & p(n, \theta_2) & \cdots & p(n, \theta_m) \\ p(n, \theta_1 + \Delta_1) & p(n, \theta_2 + \Delta_1) & \cdots & p(n, \theta_m + \Delta_1) \\ \cdots & \cdots & \cdots & \cdots \\ p(n, \theta_1 + \Delta_{m-1}) & p(n, \theta_2 + \Delta_{m-1}) & \cdots & p(n, \theta_m + \Delta_{m-1}) \end{vmatrix}$$

and

$$D'' = \begin{vmatrix} P(0, t_1 - \theta_1) & P(n_1, t_1 - \theta_1) & \cdots & P(n_{m-1}, t_1 - \theta_1) \\ P(0, t_1 - \theta_2) & P(n_1, t_1 - \theta_2) & \cdots & P(n_{m-1}, t_1 - \theta_2) \\ \cdots\cdots & \cdots\cdots & \cdots & \cdots\cdots \\ P(0, t_1 - \theta_m) & P(n_1, t_1 - \theta_m) & \cdots & P(n_{m-1}, t_1 - \theta_m) \end{vmatrix}$$

from (13, p. 48, prob. 68).

Then sign $D' = 0$ or $(-1)^{m(m-1)/2}$ since:

(a) $0 > -\Delta_1 > -\Delta_2 > \cdots -\Delta_{m-1}$.

(b) Reversing the order of the rows in D' multiplies D' by $(-1)^{m(m-1)/2}$.

(c) The resulting determinant ≥ 0 by Lemma 3.2.

Consider D''.

(a) If $t_1 \leq \theta_i$, $i = 1, 2, \cdots, m - 1$, then all rows of D'' from the ith row on consist of all 1's, so that $D'' = 0$.

(b) If $t_1 > \theta_m$, then the first column of D'' consists of 0's, so that $D'' = 0$.

(c) If $\theta_{m-1} < t_1 \leq \theta_m$, then

$$D'' = \begin{vmatrix} 0 & P(n_1, t_1 - \theta_1) & \cdots & P(n_{m-1}, t_1 - \theta_1) \\ 0 & P(n_1, t_1 - \theta_2) & \cdots & P(n_{m-1}, t_1 - \theta_2) \\ \vdots & \vdots & \vdots & \vdots \\ 0 & P(n_1, t_1 - \theta_{m-1}) & \cdots & P(n_{m-1}, t_1 - \theta_{m-1}) \\ 1 & 1 & \cdots & 1 \end{vmatrix}$$

By inductive hypothesis, sign $D'' = 0$ or $(-1)^{(m-1)}(-1)^{(m-1)(m-2)/2} = (-1)^{m(m-1)/2}$.

Thus, in general, the integrand of (3.2) is ≥ 0. Hence $P(n, t)$ is PT_m.   QED

A similar theorem holds for $p(n, t)$.

Theorem 3.2. If $f(t)$ is Pff_k having a continuous first derivative, with $f(t) = 0$ for $t < 0$, then $p(n, t)$ is PT_k where $n = 1, 2, \cdots$.

Proof. First we prove $p(n, t)$ is PT_2. Let $0 < n_1 < n_2$,

$t_1 < t_2$, and $d_2 = \begin{vmatrix} p(n_1, t_1) & p(n_1, t_2) \\ p(n_2, t_1) & p(n_2, t_2) \end{vmatrix}$.

(a) For $t_1 < 0$, the first column of d_2 consists of 0's, so that $d_2 = 0$.

(b) Let $t_1 \geq 0$. Write

$$d_2 = \int \begin{vmatrix} p(n_1, t_1) & p(n_1, t_1 - \theta) \\ p(n_1, t_2) & p(n_1, t_1 - \theta) \end{vmatrix} p(n_2 - n_1, \theta) d\theta \geq 0$$

by Lemma 3.2.

Assume we have shown $p(n, t)$ is PT_{m-1} for $m \leq k$. We shall show that this implies $p(n, t)$ is PT_m. This in turn will imply that $p(n, t)$ is PT_k.

Let $0 < n_1 < n_2 < \cdots < n_m, t_1 < t_2 < \cdots < t_m$. Define

$$d_m = \begin{vmatrix} p(n, t_1) & p(n + n_1, t_1) & \cdots & p(n + n_{m-1}, t_1) \\ p(n, t_2) & p(n + n_1, t_2) & \cdots & p(n + n_{m-1}, t_2) \\ \vdots & \vdots & & \vdots \\ p(n, t_m) & p(n + n_1, t_m) & \cdots & p(n + n_{m-1}, t_m) \end{vmatrix}$$

$$\Delta_j = t_{j+1} - t_1, j = 1, 2, \cdots, k - 1,$$

$$p_r(0, t) = \begin{cases} r & \text{for } 0 \leq t \leq \dfrac{1}{r} \\ 0 & \text{otherwise} \end{cases}$$

and

$$d_{m,r} = \begin{vmatrix} \int p(n, \theta) p_r(0, t_1 - \theta) d\theta & p(n + n_1, t_1) \\ & \cdots \quad p(n + n_{m-1}, t_1) \\ \int p(n, \theta + \Delta_1) p_r(0, t_1 - \theta) d\theta & p(n + n_1, t_2) \\ & \cdots \quad p(n + n_{m-1}, t_2) \\ \vdots & \\ \int p(n, \theta + \Delta_{m-1}) p_r(0, t_1 - \theta) d\theta & p(n + n_1, t_m) \\ & \cdots \quad p(n + n_{m-1}, t_m) \end{vmatrix} \quad (3.3)$$

Then

$$d_{m,r} = \begin{vmatrix} \int p(n, \theta) p_r(0, t_1 - \theta) d\theta & \int p(n, \theta) p(n_1, t_1 - \theta) d\theta \\ \int p(n, \theta + \Delta_1) p_r(0, t_1 - \theta) d\theta & \int p(n, \theta + \Delta_1) p(n_1, t_1 - \theta) d\theta \\ \vdots & \vdots \\ \int p(n, \theta + \Delta_{m-1}) p_r(0, t_1 - \theta) d\theta & \int p(n, \theta + \Delta_{m-1}) p(n_1, t_1 - \theta) d\theta \\ & \cdots \quad \int p(n, \theta) p(n_{m-1}, t_1 - \theta) d\theta \\ & \cdots \quad \int p(n, \theta + \Delta_1) p(n_{m-1}, t_1 - \theta) d\theta \\ & \vdots \\ & \cdots \quad \int p(n, \theta + \Delta_{m-1}) p(n_{m-1}, t_1 - \theta) d\theta \end{vmatrix}$$

$$= \int_{\theta_1 < \cdots < \theta_m} \cdots \int d' d''_r d\theta_1 \cdots d\theta_m, \text{ where}$$

$$d' = \begin{vmatrix} p(n, \theta_1) & p(n, \theta_2) & \cdots & p(n, \theta_m) \\ p(n, \theta_1 + \Delta_1) & p(n, \theta_2 + \Delta_1) & \cdots & p(n, \theta_m + \Delta_1) \\ \vdots & \vdots & & \vdots \\ p(n, \theta_1 + \Delta_{m-1}) & p(n, \theta_2 + \Delta_{m-1}) & \cdots & p(n, \theta_m + \Delta_{m-1}) \end{vmatrix},$$

$$d_r'' = \begin{vmatrix} p_r(0,\, t_1 - \theta_1) & p(n_1,\, t_1 - \theta_1) & \cdots & p(n_{m-1},\, t_1 - \theta_1) \\ p_r(0,\, t_1 - \theta_2) & p(n_1,\, t_1 - \theta_2) & \cdots & p(n_{m-1},\, t_1 - \theta_2) \\ \vdots & \vdots & & \vdots \\ p_r(0,\, t_1 - \theta_m) & p(n_1,\, t_1 - \theta_m) & \cdots & p(n_{m-1},\, t_1 - \theta_m) \end{vmatrix}$$

by (13, p. 48, prob. 68).

By Lemma 3.2, sign $d' = 0$ or $(-1)^{m(m-1)/2}$.

Consider d_r''.

(a) If $t_1 < \theta_m$, the last row of d_r'' consists of 0's, so that $d_r'' = 0$.

(b) If $t_1 > \theta_m + \dfrac{1}{r}$, the first column of d_r'' consists of 0's, so that $d_r'' = 0$.

(c) Let $\theta_m \le t_1 \le \theta_m + \dfrac{1}{r}$. Let $N_r =$ set of $\theta = (\theta_1, \cdots, \theta_m)$ such that $0 \le \theta_m - \theta_{m-1} \le \dfrac{1}{r}$. Then for θ not in N_r,

$$d_r'' = \begin{vmatrix} 0 & p(n_1,\, t_1 - \theta_1) & \cdots & p(n_{m-1},\, t_1 - \theta_1) \\ 0 & p(n_1,\, t_1 - \theta_2) & \cdots & p(n_{m-1},\, t_1 - \theta_2) \\ \vdots & \vdots & & \vdots \\ 0 & p(n_1,\, t_1 - \theta_{m-1}) & \cdots & p(n_{m-1},\, t_1 - \theta_{m-1}) \\ 1 & p(n_1,\, t_1 - \theta_m) & \cdots & p(n_{m-1},\, t_1 - \theta_m) \end{vmatrix}$$

By inductive hypothesis, the last determinant is 0 or has sign $(-1)^{m(m-1)/2}$.

Thus for θ not in N_r, the integrand $d'd_r'' \ge 0$. Hence $d_{m,r} \ge \int_{N_r} \cdots \int d'd_r'' d\theta_1 \cdots d\theta_m$, with the measure of $N_r \le t_1^{m-1} \cdot \dfrac{1}{r}$.

We may write, for θ in N_r

$$d'd_r'' = \begin{vmatrix} p(n, \theta_1) & \cdots & p(n, \theta_{m-1}) & \dfrac{p(n, \theta_m) - p(n, \theta_{m-1})}{1/r} \\ \vdots & & \vdots & \vdots \\ p(n, \theta_1 + \Delta_{m-1}) & \cdots & p(n, \theta_{m-1} + \Delta_{m-1}) & \\ & & & \dfrac{p(n, \theta_m + \Delta_{m-1}) - p(n, \theta_{m-1} + \Delta_{m-1})}{1/r} \end{vmatrix}$$

$$\cdot \begin{vmatrix} \delta_r(t_1 - \theta_1) & p(n_1,\, t_1 - \theta_1) & \cdots & p(n_{m-1},\, t_1 - \theta_1) \\ \vdots & \vdots & & \vdots \\ \delta_r(t_1 - \theta_m) & p(n_1,\, t_1 - \theta_m) & \cdots & p(n_{m-1},\, t_1 - \theta_m) \end{vmatrix}$$

where $\delta_r(u) = \begin{cases} 1 & \text{for } 0 \le u \le \dfrac{1}{r}. \\ 0 & \text{otherwise} \end{cases}$

Since $0 \le \theta_m - \theta_{m-1} \le \dfrac{1}{r}$, given $\epsilon > 0$, there exists r_0 such that for all $r \geq r_0$,

$$\left| \frac{p(n, \theta_m) - p(n, \theta_{m-1})}{1/r} \right| \leq \left| \frac{dp(n, \theta)}{d\theta} \right|_{\theta = \theta'} + \epsilon, \; \theta_{m-1} \leq \theta' \leq \theta_m.$$

Since $f(t)$ has a continuous first derivative, $\dfrac{dp(n, \theta)}{d\theta}$ is continuous

on $[0, t_1]$; hence $\left| \dfrac{dp(n, \theta)}{d\theta} \right|_{\theta = \theta'} + \epsilon$ is bounded by some constant

M_1 for all $r \geq r_0$, all $\theta_m \leq t_1$. Similarly, the ith entry of the last column of the first determinant is bounded by some M_i, $i = 1, 2,$ $\cdots, m$. Since $p(n, \theta)$ is continuous on $[0, \theta_{m-1} + \Delta_{m-1}]$, a common bound M exists for all the other entries of the first determinant, for $0 \leq \theta_m \leq t_1$. Hence the first determinant is bounded by $m!$ $\cdot M^{m-1} \max_{i=1, \ldots, m} M_i$, independent of r.

Similarly we can demonstrate a bound independent of r for the second determinant. Hence $d' \, d''$ is bounded, independent of r, so that by letting $r \to \infty$, we see that $\int_{N_r} \cdots \int d' \, d'' \, d\theta_1 \cdots d\theta_m \to 0$. Hence $\lim_{r \to \infty} d_{m,r} \geq 0$.

But returning to (3.3), we see that $\lim_{r \to \infty} d_{m,r} = d_m$. Hence $p(n, t)$ is PT_m. $\hspace{2em}$ QED

In addition to their use in the present problem, Theorems 3.1 and 3.2 are of interest in renewal theory. We will discuss further consequences of these theorems in subsequent chapters.

As a consequence of Theorem 3.1, we obtain:

Theorem 3.3. If f is Pff_2 with $f(t) = 0$ for $t < 0$, then $P(n, t)$ is Pff_2 in n for each $t \geq 0$.

Proof. For $t = 0$, $P(n, t) = \begin{cases} 0 & \text{for } n < 0 \\ 1 & \text{for } n \geq 0. \end{cases}$

Hence by an argument similar to that of Lemma 3.3, $P(n, t)$ may be proved to be Pff_2.

For $t > 0$, $n_1 < n_2$, and $m_1 < m_2$, let

$$D = \begin{vmatrix} P(n_1 - m_1, t) & P(n_1 - m_2, t) \\ P(n_2 - m_1, t) & P(n_2 - m_2, t) \end{vmatrix}.$$

(a) If $n_1 \leq m_2$, $P(n_1 - m_2, t) = 0$. Thus $D \geq 0$.

(b) Assume $n_1 > m_2$. Thus $m_1 < m_2 < n_1 < n_2$. Then

$$D = \int \begin{vmatrix} P(n_1 - m_1, t) & P(n_1 - m_2, t) \\ P(n_1 - m_1, t - \theta) & P(n_1 - m_2, t - \theta) \end{vmatrix} p(n_2 - n_1, \theta) d\theta.$$

Since the determinant in the integrand ≥ 0 by Theorem 3.1, $D \geq 0$.   QED

For $n = 0, 1, 2, \cdots$, define $\Delta P(n, t) = P(n + 1, t) - P(n, t)$. We show that:

Theorem 3.4. If f is Pff_2 with $f(t) = 0$ for $t < 0$, then $\Delta P(n, t)$ is PT_2.

Proof. $\Delta P(n, t) = P(n + 1, t) - P(n, t) = \int p(n, \theta)$ $\cdot \{P(1, t - \theta) - P(0, t - \theta)\} d\theta = \int p(n, \theta) \Delta P(0, t - \theta) d\theta$. If we show $\Delta P(0, t - \theta)$ is Pff_2 in the second argument, then by applying Lemma 3.1, the conclusion will follow.

For $t_1 < t_2, \theta_1 < \theta_2$, define

$$D = \begin{vmatrix} \Delta P(0, t_1 - \theta_1) & \Delta P(0, t_1 - \theta_2) \\ \Delta P(0, t_2 - \theta_1) & \Delta P(0, t_2 - \theta_2) \end{vmatrix}.$$

(a) If $t_1 \leq \theta_1$, then $\Delta P(0, t_1 - \theta_1) = 1 - 1 = 0$, and $\Delta P(0, t_1 - \theta_2) = 1 - 1 = 0$. Thus $D = 0$.

(b) If $\theta_1 < t_1 < t_2 \leq \theta_2$, then $\Delta P(0, t_1 - \theta_2) = 1 - 1 = 0$, and $\Delta P(0, t_2 - \theta_2) = 1 - 1 = 0$. Thus $D = 0$.

(c) If $\theta_1 < t_1 \leq \theta_2 < t_2$, then $\Delta P(0, t_1 - \theta_2) = 1 - 1 = 0$, while $\Delta P(0, t_1 - \theta_1) \geq 0$ and $\Delta P(0, t_2 - \theta_2) \geq 0$. Hence, $D \geq 0$.

(d) If $\theta_1 < \theta_2 < t_1 < t_2$, then

$$D = \begin{vmatrix} P(1, t_1 - \theta_1) & P(1, t_1 - \theta_2) \\ P(1, t_2 - \theta_1) & P(1, t_2 - \theta_2) \end{vmatrix} \geq 0 \qquad \text{by Theorem 3.1.}$$

Note that all possibilities are covered: (a) implies that only $\theta_1 < t_1 < t_2$ need be considered; and (b), (c), and (d) respectively show $D \geq 0$ for $t_2 \leq \theta_2$, $t_1 \leq \theta_2 < t_2$, and $\theta_2 < t_1$.

Thus $\Delta P(n, t)$ is PT_2.   QED

Theorem 3.4 immediately yields:

Theorem 3.5. If f is Pff_2 with $f(t) = 0$ for $t < 0$, then $\Delta P(n, t)$ is Pff_2 in n.

Proof. Let $n_1 < n_2$, $m_1 < m_2$.

Define

$$D = \begin{vmatrix} \Delta P(n_1 - m_1, t) & \Delta P(n_1 - m_2, t) \\ \Delta P(n_2 - m_1, t) & \Delta P(n_2 - m_2, t) \end{vmatrix}$$

(a) If $n_1 < m_2$, $\Delta P(n_1 - m_2, t) = 0$. Thus $D \geq 0$.

(b) Let $n_1 \geq m_2$. Thus $m_1 < m_2 \leq n_1 < n_2$.

Then

$$D = \int \begin{vmatrix} \Delta P(n_1 - m_2, t - \theta) & \Delta P(n_1 - m_2, t) \\ \Delta P(n_2 - m_2, t - \theta) & \Delta P(n_2 - m_2, t) \end{vmatrix} p(m_2 - m_1, \theta)d\theta \geq 0$$

since the determinant of the integrand ≥ 0 by Theorem 3.4.   QED

Let us now return to the inventory problem motivating the whole line of development above.

Theorem 3.6. If the probability densities $f_{ij}(t)$, $j = 1, \cdots, d_i$; $i = 1, \cdots, k$; for the length of life t of a single unit are Pff_2, then $q_i(n)$, the probability density for the total number n of units of the ith type failing during $[0, t_0]$, is Pff_2 in n, for $i = 1, \cdots, k$.

Proof. $q_i(n)$ is obtained as the convolution of the densities for the number of replacements of component i, j for $j = 1, \cdots, d_i$. By Theorem 3.4, each such density is Pff_2 in n, and by Lemma 3.1, the convolution of Pff_2 densities is Pff_2.   QED

Recall that $Q_i(n) = \sum_{m=0}^{n} q_i(m)$; i.e., $Q_i(n)$ represents the probability of experiencing a total of at most n failures in the d_i sockets. Then, we characterize $Q_i(n)$ in:

Theorem 3.7. If $f_{ij}(t)$ are Pff_2 for $j = 1, \cdots, d_i$, then $Q_i(n)$ is Pff_2 in n.

Proof. Write $Q_i(n) = \sum_{m=0}^{\infty} q_i(m) H'(n - m)$, where

$$H'(r) = \begin{cases} 1 & \text{for } r = 0, 1, 2, \cdots \\ 0 & \text{for } r = -1, -2, \cdots \end{cases}$$

Then by the same argument as in Lemma 3.3, $H'(r)$ is Pff_2 in r, where r takes on integer values. Since $Q_i(n)$ is the convolution of two Pff_2 functions $Q_i(n)$ is Pff_2 in n.   QED

As a result, we get:

Theorem 3.8. If the $f_{ij}(t)$ are Pff_2 for $j = 1, \cdots, d_i$, then $Q_i(n + 1)/Q_i(n)$ and $\Delta R_i(n)$ are decreasing functions of n, where $n = 0, 1, 2, \cdots$.

Proof. $\Delta R_i(n) = \ln Q_i(n + 1) - \ln Q_i(n) = \ln \{Q_i(n + 1)/ Q_i(n)\}$. By Theorem 3.7, $Q_i(n + 1)/Q_i(n)$ is decreasing in n. Hence $\Delta R_i(n)$ is decreasing in n.   QED

The climax of this long line of reasoning may be stated in:

Theorem 3.9. If the underlying failure densities $f_{ij}, j = 1, \cdots, d_i; \ i = 1, \cdots, k;$ are Pff_2, then Procedures 1 and 2 of Section 2.1 yield the optimal spare parts kits. That is, the hypothesis of Theorem 2.1 holds, so that the conclusion and corollary follow.

The actual computation involved in obtaining the $Q_i(n)$ in the general case will be tedious, except in the case of exponential life distributions (Chapter 6). In general, an electronic computer would probably be needed.

CHAPTER 4

Extensions of the Theoretical Results

In this chapter, we extend some of the theorems of Chapter 3. Using these extensions, we will see that Procedures 1 and 2 of Section 2.1 yield the solutions to a more general inventory model than the one originally stated.

4.1. Convolution of Non-Identical Densities

If we examine the proofs of Theorems 3.1 and 3.2, we note that the successive convolutions yielding $p(n, t)$ and $P(n, t)$ need not necessarily refer to a common density. Let us therefore define $p'(n, t) = f_1 * f_2 * \cdots * f_n(t)$, the n-fold convolution of successive densities f_i, $i = 1, 2, \cdots$,

$$P'(n, t) = \int_t^\infty p'(n, u)du$$

and

$$\Delta P'(n, t) = P'(n + 1, t) - P'(n, t)$$

Thus $p'(n, t)$, $P'(n, t)$, and $\Delta P'(n, t)$ are analogous to $p(n, t)$, $P(n, t)$, and $\Delta P(n, t)$, the only difference being that the successive densities convoluted need not be the same.

We now present generalizations of earlier results, using the newly defined functions.

Lemma 4.1.   If $f_i(t)$ is Pff_k with $f_i(t) = 0$ for $t < 0$, $i = 1, 2$, $\cdots$, then $p'(n, t)$ is Pff_k in t for $n = 1, 2, \cdots$.

Proof. As before, repeated application of Lemma 3.1 yields the conclusion.

Lemma 4.2.   If $f_i(t)$ is Pff_k with $f_i(t) = 0$ for $t < 0$, $i = 1, 2$, $\cdots$, then $P'(n, t)$ is Pff_k in t for $n = 1, 2, \cdots$.

Proof. The proof is as in Lemma 3.4.

Theorem 4.1.   If $f_i(t)$ is Pff_k with $f_i(t) = 0$ for $t < 0$, $i = 1, 2$, $\cdots$, then $P'(n, t)$ is PT_k, where n ranges over the values $0, 1, 2, \cdots$.

Proof. The proof consists of the same arguments as in Theorem 3.1. The only difference is that p' and P' replace p and P respectively — with one slight adjustment. In writing the analogue of (3.1), the quantity $p'(n_2 - n_1, \theta)$ must refer to the convolution of densities $f_{n_1+1}, \cdots, f_{n_2}$ (rather than $f_1, \cdots, f_{n_2-n_1}$). Similarly the quantities $P'(n_i, t_1 - \theta_j)$ appearing in the analogue of (3.2) must refer to the convolutions of densities $f_{n+1}, \cdots, f_{n+n_i}$ (rather than $f_1, \cdots, f_{n_i}$. These adjustments do not affect the validity of the arguments however.

Theorem 4.2.   If $f_i(t)$ is Pff_k with continuous first derivative, and $f_i(t) = 0$ for $t < 0$, $i = 1, 2, \cdots$, then $p'(n, t)$ is PT_k, where n ranges over the values $0, 1, 2, \cdots$.

Theorem 4.3.   If $f_i(t)$ is Pff_2 with $f_i(t) = 0$ for $t < 0$, $i = 1, 2$, $\cdots$, then $P'(n, t)$ is Pff_2 in n for each $t \geq 0$, where $P'(n, t)$ is defined $= 0$ for $n < 0$.

Theorem 4.4.   If $f_i(t)$ is Pff_2 with $f_i(t) = 0$ for $t < 0$, $i = 1, 2$, $\cdots$, then $\Delta P'(n, t)$ is PT_2.

Theorem 4.5.   If $f_i(t)$ is Pff_2 with $f_i(t) = 0$ for $t < 0$, $i = 1, 2$, $\cdots$, then $\Delta P'(n, t)$ is Pff_2 in n.

The proofs of Theorems 4.2 through 4.5 are as in the corresponding theorems in Chapter 3, with the adjustments described in the proof of Theorem 4.1.

These generalizations permit us to state that Procedures 1 and 2 of Section 2.1 for obtaining the optimal spares kits (see Theorem 3.9) apply even when the successive replacements of a given component have *different* (known) failure distributions. At first glance, this may seem like a generalization of little application, since in most cases successive replacements of any one component will be made with units having a common failure distribution. However, if at the beginning of the period, the components already in the system have been aged by previous use, the (conditional) distribution of remaining life is different from the distribution of life of future replacements (except only in the case of exponential life distributions). Another possibility is that replacements may be of different known ages. In this connection, it is helpful to note that the conditional probability density for the remaining life t of a component given its age t_0 is Pff_2 if the underlying density is Pff_2; i.e.:

Theorem 4.6. If $f(t)$ is Pff_2 with $f(t) = 0$ for $t < 0$, then

$$g(t) = \begin{cases} 0 & \text{for } t < 0 \\ \dfrac{f(t_0 + t)}{\displaystyle\int_{t_0}^{\infty} f(u)\,du} & \text{for } t \geq 0 \end{cases} \qquad \text{is } Pff_2.$$

Proof. Let $t_1 < t_2$, $\theta_1 < \theta_2$.
Define

$$D = \begin{vmatrix} g(t_1 - \theta_1) & g(t_1 - \theta_2) \\ g(t_2 - \theta_1) & g(t_2 - \theta_2) \end{vmatrix}$$

$$D' = \frac{1}{\displaystyle\int_{t_0}^{\infty} f(u)\,du} \begin{vmatrix} f(t_0 + t_1 - \theta_1) & f(t_0 + t_1 - \theta_2) \\ f(t_0 + t_2 - \theta_1) & f(t_0 + t_2 - \theta_2) \end{vmatrix}.$$

Then if $t_1 \geq \theta_2$, $D = D'$. Thus sign $D = $ sign $D' \geq 0$ since f is Pff_2. If $t_1 < \theta_2$, then $g(t_1 - \theta_2) = 0$ by definition, so that $D \geq 0$.   QED

We close this section with an application of Theorem 4.2 to

obtain the following characterization of *compound* distributions, not related to our inventory problem:

Theorem 4.7. Let $X_i \geq 0$ be distributed with density $f_i(t)$, a Pff_k, $i = 1, 2, \cdots$.
Define

$$S_N = \sum_{i=1}^{N} X_i$$

where N is a random variable independent of X_1, X_2, $\cdots$, with density $g(n, \mu)$, where μ is a parameter, and g is PT_k. Then $r(t, \mu)$, the probability density for S_N, is PT_k.

Proof.

$$r(t, \mu) = \sum_{n=1}^{\infty} P[N = n]f_{1*} \cdots *f_n(t) = \sum_{n=1}^{\infty} g(n, \mu)p'(n, t)$$

By Theorem 4.1, $p'(n, t)$ is PT_k. Hence by Lemma 3.1, $r(t, \mu)$ is PT_k.   QED

For example, consider a Poisson process with parameter 1 as describing the occurrence of events. If μ is the time elapsed since the start of the process, $g(n, \mu) = (e^{-\mu}\mu^n)/n!$. If at the time the nth event occurs, a random variable $X_n \geq 0$ with density $f_n(t)$, a Pff_k, is observed, then the cumulative random variable, $S_N = \sum_{i=1}^{N} X_i$ has a PT_k density (in t and μ).

4.2. Scheduled Times Random

Suppose the t_{ij} are not constants but positive random variables T_{ij} with corresponding Pff_2 densities $g_{ij}(t)$, $j = 1, \cdots , d_i$; $i = 1, \cdots , k$. We shall show that when $d_i = 1$, $i = 1, \cdots , k$ (only one operating component of each type), the probability density for the number of replacements of component i during $[0, t_i]$ is Pff_2, so that by the arguments of Theorem 3.7, 3.8, and 3.9 we may conclude that Procedures 1 and 2 of Section 2.1 yield optimal spare parts kits, as before.

We shall drop the subscript i in what follows.
Define

$$\Phi(n, \omega) = \begin{cases} 0 & \text{for } n < 0 \\ \text{probability that the sum of } n+1 \text{ independent observa-} \\ \text{tions from } f(t) \text{ exceeds } T \text{ by at least } \omega, \text{ where} \\ -\infty < \omega < \infty, \text{ for } n = 0, 1, 2, \cdots \end{cases}$$

Then

$$\Phi(n, \omega) = \int P(n+1, t)g(t - \omega)dt \qquad \text{for } n = 0, 1, 2, \cdots$$

Thus, since $P(n, t)$ is PT_2 by Theorem 3.1 and $g(t)$ is Pff_2 by assumption, we conclude that $\Phi(n, \omega)$ is PT_2 (where n ranges over 0, 1, 2, $\cdots$) by Lemma 3.1.

Next we shall show $\Phi(n, \omega)$ is Pff_2 in n for each fixed real ω. Let $n_1 < n_2,\ m_1 < m_2$.
Define

$$D = \begin{vmatrix} \Phi(n_1 - m_1, \omega) & \Phi(n_1 - m_2, \omega) \\ \Phi(n_2 - m_1, \omega) & \Phi(n_2 - m_2, \omega) \end{vmatrix}$$

(a) If $n_1 < m_2$, then $\Phi(n_1 - m_2, \omega) = 0$ by definition. Hence $D \geq 0$.

(b) Assume $m_1 < m_2 \leq n_1 < n_2$. Thus, we may write

$$D = \int \begin{vmatrix} \Phi(n_1 - m_1, \omega) & \Phi(n_1 - m_2, \omega) \\ \Phi(n_1 - m_1, \omega - \theta) & \Phi(n_1 - m_2, \omega - \theta) \end{vmatrix} p(n_2 - n_1, \theta)d\theta$$

But the determinant in the integrand ≥ 0 since $\Phi(n, \omega)$ is PT_2, (where n ranges over 0, 1, 2, $\cdots$). Hence $\Phi(n, \omega)$ is Pff_2 in n for each fixed real ω.

Thus $\Phi(n+1, \omega)/\Phi(n, \omega)$ decreases in n for fixed ω. But $\Phi(n, 0)$ represents the probability that n or less spares will be required during $[0, T]$. Using the arguments of Theorems 3.7, 3.8, and 3.9, the monotonicity of the ratio $\Phi(n+1, 0)/\Phi(n, 0)$ is sufficient to insure that Procedures 1 and 2 yield optimal spare parts kits.

CHAPTER 5

Exponential Failure Distributions

5.1. Explicit Solution

In the case of a complex electronic system, the component failure distribution usually assumed is the exponential. We shall now obtain an explicit solution of the inventory problem (Section 1.1) for this case, and present an illustration of it.

Assume then, that

$$f_{ij}(t) = \begin{cases} 0 & \text{for } t < 0 \\ \mu_{ij}e^{-\mu_{ij}t} & \text{for } t \geq 0 \end{cases}$$

where μ_{ij} represents the failure rate per unit of time, $j = 1, \cdots, d_i$; $i = 1, \cdots, k$. It follows immediately that

$$\Delta P_{ij}(n, t_{ij}) = e^{-\mu_{ij}t_{ij}}(\mu_{ij}t_{ij})^n/n!$$

a Poisson density with parameter $\mu_{ij}t_{ij}$ (1, p. 272). Next note that

$$q_i(n) = e^{-\lambda_i}\lambda_i^n/n! \qquad (5.1)$$

where $\lambda_i = \sum_{j=1}^{d_i} \mu_{ij}t_{ij}$, since the convolution of Poisson densities is a Poisson density with parameter given by the sum of the separate parameters (2, p. 205).

We know that the exponential density is Pff_∞ (9, p. 125). Hence Procedures 1 and 2 yield the optimal spare parts kits by Theorem 3.9. In this connection, it is interesting to give a separate proof that $\Delta R_i(n)$ is a decreasing function of n for fixed t, the condition needed to apply Theorem 3.9.

Theorem 5.1. If $f_{ij}(t) = \begin{cases} 0 & \text{for } t < 0 \\ \mu_{ij}e^{-\mu_{ij}t} & \text{for } t \geq 0 \end{cases}$,

$j = 1, \cdots, d_i$, then $\Delta R_i(n)$ is a decreasing function of n.

Proof. Dropping subscripts,

$\Delta R(n) = \ln\{Q(n+1)/Q(n)\}$

$$= \ln\{1 + [\lambda^{n+1}/(n+1)!]/\sum_{j=0}^{n}[\lambda^j/j!]\}$$

It is sufficient to show that $g(n, \lambda) = [\lambda^{n+1}/(n+1)!]/\sum_{j=0}^{n}[\lambda^j/j!]$ is a decreasing function of n for all $\lambda > 0$.

Now $g(n, \lambda) - g(n-1, \lambda)$ has the same sign as

$$f(n, \lambda) = \lambda\sum_{j=0}^{n-1}\lambda^j/j! - (n+1)\sum_{j=0}^{n}\lambda^j/j!$$

But, after simplification,

$$df(n, \lambda)/d\lambda = f(n-1, \lambda) \tag{5.2}$$

with $f(1, \lambda) = -2 - \lambda < 0$ for $\lambda > 0$. Suppose $f(n, \lambda) < 0$ for $n = 1, 2, \cdots, n_0 - 1$. Then $df(n_0, \lambda)/d\lambda < 0$ for $\lambda > 0$ by (5.2). Since $f(n_0, 0) = -(n_0 + 1) < 0$ and $df(n_0, \lambda)/d\lambda < 0$, then $f(n_0, \lambda) < 0$ for all $\lambda > 0$. By induction, $f(n, \lambda) < 0$ for $n = 1, 2, \cdots; \lambda > 0$. Thus $g(n, \lambda)$ is a decreasing function of n for $\lambda > 0$.

A useful approximation in the case of exponential failure distributions may be derived as follows:

$$\Delta R_i(n) = \ln\left\{1 + \frac{\lambda_i^{n+1}e^{-\lambda_i}}{(n+1)!}\bigg/\sum_{j=0}^{n}\frac{\lambda_i^j e^{-\lambda_i}}{j!}\right\}$$

For n such that $\sum_{j=0}^{n}\dfrac{\lambda_i^j e^{-\lambda_i}}{j!}$ is close to 1, and hence

$\dfrac{\lambda_i^{n+1}e^{-\lambda_i}}{(n+1)!}$ close to 0, we may write

$$\Delta R_i(n) \approx \frac{\lambda_i^{n+1}e^{-\lambda_i}}{(n+1)!}\bigg/\sum_{j=0}^{n}\frac{\lambda_i^j e^{-\lambda_i}}{j!},$$

so that

$$\Delta R_i(n) \approx \frac{\lambda_i^{n+1} e^{-\lambda_i}}{(n+1)!} \tag{5.3}$$

Since the latter expression is tabulated (11), the computation of Procedures 1 or 2 is simple even with only a desk calculator.

5.2. Illustration

A UHF receiving system and a VHF receiving system are to be placed in the field for a three months period of experimentation. The essential tubes in the two systems are described in Table 1.

TABLE 1

i	Tube type	Failure rate/hour	c_i, cost per tube ($)	Number in UHF, scheduled for 332 hours of use each	Number in VHF, scheduled for 2160 hours of use each	λ_i, expected number of failures
1	Radechon	1/2500	240	4	4	4.0
2	Memotron	1/4000	1025	2	5	2.9
3	Carcinotron	1/800	1158	4	0	1.7
4	TWT	1/6000	750	2	0	0.11

During the period of operation in the field, the UHF tubes are each scheduled for 332 hours of use and the VHF tubes are each scheduled for 2160 hours of use. Assuming an exponential life distribution for each of the tube types with failure rate as shown above, and assuming independence of operation of the tubes, find an optimal allocation of spare parts for various spares budgets, i.e., an allocation which maximizes assurance of continued system operation during the period in the field.

First, we compute the expected number of spares of each type used during the period:

$$\lambda_1 = 1/2500 \quad \{4 \cdot 332 + 4 \cdot 2160\} = 4.0$$
$$\lambda_2 = 1/4000 \quad \{2 \cdot 332 + 5 \cdot 2160\} = 2.9$$
$$\lambda_3 = 1/800 \quad \{4 \cdot 332\} = 1.7$$
$$\lambda_4 = 1/6000 \quad \{2 \cdot 332\} = 0.11$$

One way to determine the first value of r to use is to compute $\lambda_1 + 3\sqrt{\lambda_1}$ and round to the nearest integer, obtaining 10. Let $n_1^* = 10$. Thus n_1^* corresponds to a value three standard deviations above the mean. (In a Poisson distribution the standard deviation equals the square root of the mean.)

Using the approximation (5.3), we let r be determined from

$$r = \frac{1}{c_1} e^{-\lambda_1} \frac{\lambda_1^{10}}{10!} = .000022. \qquad \text{(Molina's Table I, 11.)}$$

We then find n_2^* as the largest value of n such that

$$\frac{1}{c_2} e^{-\lambda_2} \frac{\lambda_2^n}{n!} \geq .000022 \qquad (5.4)$$

Using Molina's Table I (11), we find $n_2^* = 6$.

Replacing the subscript 2 in (5.4) by 3 and 4 respectively and proceeding similarly, we find $n_3^* = 4$ and $n_4^* = 1$.

From $n^* = 10, 6, 4, 1$, we compute

$$Q(n^*) = \prod_{i-1}^{4} \sum_{x=0}^{n_i^*} e^{-\lambda_i} \lambda_i^x / x! = .935$$

and

$$c(n^*) = \sum_{i=1}^{4} c_i n_i^* = \$13,932$$

Thus to obtain maximum assurance of continued system operation under a budget of \$13,932 for spares of the four tube types, we would stock 10 Radechons, 6 Memotrons, 4 Carcinotrons, and 1 TWT. The assurance obtained would be .935.

By taking $n_1^* = 8, 9, 11, 12$, and 13 respectively, and proceeding in a similar fashion, we would obtain the other five points plotted in Figure 1. Thus Figure 1 shows the maximum assurance of continued system operation obtainable for various given budgets for spares. In addition, the composition of the spares kit yielding the plotted maximum assurance is shown next to each point. Note that additional points lying between those shown on the optimal curve of Figure 1 may be computed as needed.

Given any value of c_0, we may read off Figure 1 the protection and composition of the optimal spare parts kit of cost not exceed-

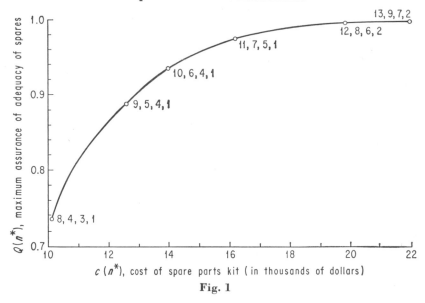

Fig. 1

ing c_0. It would be necessary to compute two successive optimal points, n^* and $n^{*(\alpha)}$, on the curve such that $c(n^*) \le c_0$, while $c(n^{*(\alpha)}) > c_0$. Then n^* would constitute the solution, the error being at most $Q(n^{*(\alpha)}) - Q(n^*)$.

5.3. Application To Reliability Design

It is interesting to note that the solution of the inventory model of Section 1.1 may be applied to a similar model in the field of reliability. Suppose we are designing a complex system (say a missile); we wish to attain maximum reliability by providing redundant units within a weight restraint. The statement of the inventory problem then describes the present reliability problem if we make certain minor modifications. Simply substitute "redundant standby unit" for "spare," "weight" for "cost." We assume, too, that replacement is made with perfect reliability.

It is then clear that the inventory problem and the present reliability problem are mathematically the same. Hence Procedures 1 and 2 of Section 2.1 yield the required number of redundant units of each component type to provide maximum reliability under a weight restraint.

Convolutions When the Random Variable Is Not Necessarily Positive

The question naturally arises: Do the theorems of Chapters 3 and 4 hold when $f(t)$ is not necessarily 0 for $t < 0$? If not, what theorems do hold? In this chapter we give a theorem somewhat analogous to Theorem 3.2.

It will be seen that when the density is not 0 for negative argument, successive convolutions have considerably weaker properties.

First we prove:

Theorem 6.1. Let $f(t)$ be Pff_m, with $f(t)$ not necessarily 0 for $t < 0$. Let $h_k(t) = \sum_{i=1}^{k} a_i \, p(n_i, \, t)$, where $n_1 < n_2 < \cdots < n_k$, $k \leq \dfrac{m+1}{2}$, and the a_i are real valued constants. Then $h_k(t)$ has $\leq 2(k - 1)$ sign changes.

Proof. Let $V(g)$ designate the number of sign changes of a function $g(t)$ as t ranges over the real line.

(a) For $k = 1$, $V\{a_1 p(n_1, t)\} = 0$, so that the theorem holds.

(b) Assume the theorem holds for $k = k_0 - 1$, where $k_0 \leq \dfrac{m+1}{2}$. We shall show that this implies that the theorem holds for $k = k_0$.

Write

$$h_{k_0}(t) = \sum_{i=1}^{k_0} a_i \, p(n_i, t) = \sum_{i=2}^{k_0} a_i \int p(n_i - n_1, \theta)p(n_1, \theta)d\theta$$
$$+ \, a_1 \lim_{r \to \infty} \int p_r(0, \theta)p(n_1, t - \theta)d\theta$$

where $p_r(0, t) = \begin{cases} r & \text{for } 0 \leq t \leq \dfrac{1}{r} \\ 0 & \text{otherwise} \end{cases}$.

Factoring, we get

$$h_{k_0}(t) = \lim_{r \to \infty} \int \left\{ \sum_{i=2}^{k_0} a_i p(n_i - n_1, \theta) + a_1 p_r(0, \theta) \right\} p(n_1, t - \theta)d\theta \quad (6.1)$$

By inductive hypothesis $\sum_{i=2}^{k_0} a_i p(n_i - n_1, \theta)$ has at most $2(k_0 - 2)$ sign changes as a function of θ. By taking r sufficiently large $a_1 p_r(0, \theta)$ can introduce at most two additional sign changes. Thus for sufficiently large r, $\sum_{i=2}^{k_0} a_i p(n_i - n_1, \theta) + a_1 p_r(0, \theta)$ has at most $2(k_0 - 1)$ sign changes. Since $p(n_1, t - \theta)$ is Pff_m, the integral on the right of (6.1) has at most $2(k_0 - 1)$ sign changes as a function of t. Taking the limit as $r \to \infty$, the number of sign changes does not increase. Hence $V(h_{k_0}) \leq 2(k_0 - 1)$.

By induction, the theorem holds for $k = 1, 2, \cdots, \dfrac{m+1}{2}$.

QED

Theorem 6.1 furnishes an interesting analogue to the fundamental variation diminishing property of a Polya Type function. From Theorem 3.2 we know that $p(n, t)$ is PT_m when $f(t)$ is Pff_m with $f(t) = 0$ for $t < 0$, with continuous first derivative. Therefore $h_k(t) = \sum_{i=1}^{k} a_i p(n_i, t)$ has at most $k - 1$ sign changes. Theorem 6.1 thus tells us that when the restriction $f(t) = 0$ for $t < 0$ is dropped, the upper bound on the number of sign changes of $h_k(t)$ becomes $2(k - 1)$ instead of $k - 1$.

Next let us use Theorem 6.1 to characterize the sign changes of $D(t_1, \cdots, t_k) = |p(n_i, t_j)|$ as a function of t_1 say, for fixed $t_2, \cdots, t_k$, $n_1, \cdots, n_k$, in the general case $f(t)$ not necessarily 0 for $t < 0$. Recall that when $f(t) = 0$ for $t < 0$, $D(t_1, \cdots, t_k)$ changes sign at most $k - 1$ times for fixed $t_2, \cdots, t_k$; $n_1, \cdots, n_k$; as t_1 varies over the whole real line (Theorem 3.2). Dropping the restriction $f(t) = 0$ for $t < 0$, we get the somewhat weaker characterization of Theorem 6.2:

Theorem 6.2. Let $f(t)$ be *Pff*$_m$ with $f(t)$ not necessarily 0 for $t < 0$. For fixed $t_2, \cdots, t_k$; $n_1, \cdots, n_k$; $k \leq \dfrac{m + 1}{2}$; $D(t_1, \cdots, t_k)$ changes sign at most $2(k - 1)$ times as t_1 ranges over $(-\infty, +\infty)$.

Proof. Write

$$D = \sum_{i=1}^{k} p(n_i, t_1) \cdot \operatorname{cof} p(n_i, t_1)$$

where $\operatorname{cof} p(n_i, t_1)$ is the cofactor of $p(n_i, t_1)$ in D, $i = 1, \cdots, k$. But $\operatorname{cof} p(n_i, t_1)$ may be considered a constant since it is a function of $t_2, \cdots, t_k$ and *not* of t_1; hence we may apply Theorem 6.1 to conclude that D has at most $2(k - 1)$ sign changes as t_1 ranges over the whole real line.   QED

Similar characterizations may be stated for $D(t_1, \cdots, t_k)$ when t_j varies while the remaining t's are fixed.

Finally, it is apparent that Theorems 6.1 and 6.2 hold when $p(n, t)$ is replaced by $p'(n, t)$, the convolution of *different Pff*$_m$ densities, $f_1, f_2, \cdots, f_n$.

BIBLIOGRAPHY

1. Arrow, Karlin, Scarf, *Studies in the Mathematical Theory of Inventory and Production*. Stanford, Calif.: Stanford University Press, 1958.

2. Cramer, *Mathematical Methods of Statistics*. Princeton, N. J.: Princeton University Press, 1946.

3. Geisler and Karr, "The Design of Military Supply Tables for Spare Parts," *Operations Research*, Vol. 4, No. 4, August, 1956, pp. 431–442.

4. Gourary, "A Simple Rule for the Consolidation of Allowance Lists," *Naval Research Logistics Quarterly*, Vol. 5, No. 1, March, 1958, pp. 1–15.

5. Gourary, "An Optimum Allowance List Model," *Naval Research Logistics Quarterly*, Vol. 3 (1956), pp. 177–191.

6. Karlin, "Polya Type Distributions IV: Some Principles of Selecting a Single Procedure from a Complete Class," *Annals of Mathematical Statistics*, Vol. 29, No. 1, March, 1958, pp. 1–21.

7. Karlin, "Polya Type Distributions III: Admissibility of Multi-action Problems," *Annals of Mathematical Statistics*, Vol. 28, No. 4, December, 1957, pp. 839–860.

8. Karlin, "Polya Type Distributions II," *Annals of Mathematical Statistics*, Vol. 28, No. 2, June, 1957, pp. 281–308.

9. Karlin, "Decision Theory for Polya Type Distributions. Case of Two Actions, I," Proceedings of the Third Berkeley Symposium on Mathematical Statistics and Probability, December, 1954, and June and July, 1955, pp. 115–128.

10. Kuhn and Tucker, "Nonlinear Programming," Proceedings of the Second Berkeley Symposium on Mathematical Statistics and Probability, 1951, pp. 481–492.

11. Molina, *Poisson's Exponential Binomial Limit*. New York: D. Van Nostrand Co., Inc., 1942.

12. Schoenberg, "On Polya Frequency Functions, I. The Totally Positive Functions and Their Laplace Transforms," *Journal D'Analyse Mathematique*, Vol. I, 1951, pp. 331–374.

13. Polya and Szego, *Ausgaben und Lehrsatze Aus Der Anslyse*, Vol. 1. Berlin: Julius Springer, 1925.